The House of
Villeroy & Boch

A philosophy and a passion:
Living and dining in the Villeroy & Boch style.

Villeroy & Boch

The name "Villeroy & Boch" is more than just a label on the bottom of a piece of china.

Villeroy & Boch is a philosophy.

One that points the way forward as the concept of "dining culture" evolves into the art of living. Not a philosophy of fixed borders, but rather one of clear lines.

"The House of Villeroy & Boch" is home to a very special frame of mind.

Expressing an openness to individual tastes and a devotion to interpreting the "finer points" of dining as integral parts of the big picture: the quintessential you.

This book is an invitation to embark on a voyage of discovery. Our aim is to transport you to the romantic world of "House & Garden," open the gates to a château nestled in the French countryside, illuminate the many facets of Paloma Picasso's stylish elegance and shower you with inspiring ideas for mixing, matching and making your own creative tableware.

And if you're curious by nature, you might just discover even more: the essence of beauty that transcends utility.

Allow us to wish you a most exhilarating journey.

House & Garden Collection
Country charm, even in the city:
A setting, a feeling and myriad interpretations.
Page 4 to 51

Château Collection
Perfection is back in vogue:
A way of life and its values.
Page 52 to 83

Paloma Picasso Collection
That's my style:
Ambience with a personal signature.
Page 84 to 99

Switch Collection
Novelty never gets old!
Ideas for playing with shape and color.
Page 100 to 113

Città & Campagna Collection
The world on your plate:
Big ideas for small budgets.
Page 114 to 123

Collection Attractions
"Seek and ye shall find":
Good things come in small packages.
Page 124 to 135

HOUSE & GAR

N COLLECTION

Fascination.

"Never before or since have I been so moved by a landscape as I was during my first time in Provence. The sight of fields of lavender in the first days of

summer, the southern sky, the fragrance of rosemary and thyme, the warmth of the people themselves – even today, I'm still fascinated by the unique combination of abundance and frugality.

It's no wonder that the charm of this setting has become a part of my lifestyle – at the table, too."

PROVENCE
lbo China,
sher safe.
l: AREZZO WHITE
y: COCO blue

In your own private
paradise, beautiful china
doesn't need to be a
forbidden fruit.
China: EDEN
Fine Vilbo China,
dishwasher safe.
Cutlery: COCO yellow

Natural beauty doesn't need to put on airs.
Simplicity has its own special charm. Welcome home!

ays you can't have
imple pleasures
on a plate?
A LA FERME
Ibo China,
sher safe.
s: DONAU
: COCO PEARL green

Morning has broken.

"When I woke with the warmth of the sun on my face,

I decided to take the day as it comes.

Best to while away the summer morning in the most

pleasant way imaginable: over cappuccino, warm croissants,

homemade jam and a little Van Morrison.

Of course, the fact that the china shares its name with

my wife is sheer coincidence.

But somehow it fits."

: JULIE
ilbo China,
asher safe.
ry: MONTCLAIR

China: WILDROSE
Faience, dishwasher safe.

How does the world define beauty?
A hint of romance. A blush of spring blossoms.
A pattern by Villeroy & Boch.

Especially a pattern with the simple grace and pastoral
charm of "Wildrose."

"Wildrose," the original among a host of imitations,
is made of faience – a type of earthenware that owes
its warm ivory tone to a special composition.

It's no wonder that "Wildrose" has countless admirers
the world over, admirers who have made this
Villeroy & Boch design a veritable cult item enjoying
sales in the millions.

The lush green leaves, hand-painted in bold brush
strokes, are the work of time-honored craftsmanship
true to its roots.

As with all Villeroy & Boch patterns, the decorative
flowers are protected by a scratch-proof glaze.
Even after hundreds of times in the dishwasher,
the soft rose petals will still look as fresh as they did
on the very first day.

"Wildrose" is a masterful mix of prettiness and
performance that is "typical Villeroy & Boch."
As the availability guarantee at least until the year
2005 attests.

In a world of vivid color, china
does well to color itself white.
For a bold, beautiful contrast.
China: **FIORI WHITE**
Bone China, dishwasher safe.
Cutlery: **ORLANDO satin finish**

Reflections on white.

"White is so pure,
so gentle – I guess people
everywhere think of it
as innocent, even virginal.

That's why it's perfect for anything to do with
weddings.

Well, first of all, I'm a man. And secondly, I've been
happily married for a long, long time. But I still
find myself drawn to white, especially when it comes
to china.

I think that people who eat with the eyes as much as
the taste buds can understand. There's no better
showcase for culinary coups than pure, perfect white."

China: CAMEO WHITE
Bone China,
dishwasher safe.
Crystal: MALINDI
Cutlery: MONTCLAIR

Pure white, pure pleasure.
Just add color – from the
garden, from the grocer,
from the panoply of life.
China, from left:
FIORI WHITE, Bone China.
ARCO WHITE, Bone China.
DAMASCO WHITE, Bone China.
MANOIR, Vitreous China.
FOGLIA, Fine Vilbo China.
All patterns dishwasher safe.

Moments in time.

"Sometimes a revelation comes out of the blue, and in a split second the mystery of life becomes crystal clear.

You just have to stay attuned to these special moments when the world comes together in an instant to form a perfect whole.

Suddenly, my heart seems to open up and embrace it all.

These are moments of pure euphoria, and I treasure them."

: MARIPOSA
China,
asher safe.
al: ALPHA
ry: TAO

Crystal.

"The other day, my friend insisted in a playful mood: 'Our tap water is so good, I can't understand why anyone would pref Chardonnay.' As for me, I'd say they both have the merits! As long as presentation is righ And that means crystal – preferably from Villeroy & Boch

Heart and soul.

"The pleasure of country life comes from the heart.
An eye for enchanting color, an affinity for
picturesque ensembles, a feel for romantic ambience.
For me, 'House & Garden' captures a feeling. At
Villeroy & Boch, 'House & Garden'
is the artistry to bring my rustic
idyll to life – with harmonious
ideas like 'Petite Fleur.'
Or another Villeroy & Boch
pattern with that characteristic
country charm."

China: PETITE FLEUR
Vitreous China,
dishwasher safe.
Crystal: OCTAVIE
Cutlery: COCO bordeaux

Summer reverie.

"Just the sound of the words puts me in mind of those warm, sunny days and the way the breeze ruffled my hair in my favorite shady spot. That summer, the courtyard of the old Spanish villa was our permanent haven, our romantic dream come true. A place where the necessities of life became life's pleasures, where pleasure was a necessity. It was a place of refuge for the soul, a home for the serenity of summer."

China: **PASADENA**
Vitreous China,
dishwasher safe.
Crystal: ALLEGORIE
Cutlery: ORLANDO
satin finish

A complete china service from Villeroy & Boch, and your happiness is complete.

You can start small, adding pieces as the spirit moves you. Or when the widening family circle makes four extra place settings a must. Or when you're a few pieces short because your little helpers got a bit too enthusiastic.

Reordering pieces or supplementing your service is no problem in the "House of Villeroy & Boch" – where the house rule is satisfaction guaranteed.

The sooner you let Villeroy & Boch know what's on your wish list, the sooner you secure your future happiness. But there's no rush – you have well into the next millennium.

Villeroy & Boch deals in firm commitments, not empty promises, offering the majority of its china and crystal series "with availability guarantee until at least 2005."

And by the way, this special service is yet another example of Villeroy & Boch's pioneering spirit.

We innovate rather than imitate.

The color of style.

"For a splash of color that's out of the ordinary, the best thing to do is hunt around in your garden. Or check out what your local florist has on hand. My friend recently arranged orange flowers around bright red gazpacho in blue bowls. The unique effect was what you might call a feast for the eyes. Tricia Guild, the guru of table arrangement, prefers harmonious ensembles. Like bougainvillea with red-tinted china. Or lavende blue blossoms alongside blue-handled knives, forks and spoons – as in this photo of 'Coco blue'."

Cutlery, from top:
MONTCLAIR
PLAY! terracotta
COCO yellow
ORLANDO satin finish
PLAY! white
COCO blue
ORLANDO satin finish

Color kaleidoscope.

"How do I remember Grandma's house?
Bright orange carrots with lunch, blackcurrants
for dessert. Sweet-smelling daffodils in a glass
vase, a whole kaleidoscope of colors blossoming
just outside the door. Bumblebees hovering by
blue elderberry, robins in the lilacs.
More than anything else, it was the vivid play
of colors that made life seem so lush back then.
And that's probably the reason I am the way
I am – always flitting like a butterfly toward
anything bright and colorful."

China: PERPIGNAN
Vitreous China,
dishwasher safe.
Cutlery: COCO yellow

Cutlery, from top:
COCO green
COCO yellow
COCO bordeaux

Conjure up a mood.
With light, color and a
sprinkling of flowers.

China: ADELINE
Fine Vilbo China,
dishwasher safe.
Crystal: VALLERY
Cutlery: COCO blue

House & Garden.

"Why is it that people today are so fond of living
the way their great-grandparents did – cherishing
steep staircases, wooden kitchen floors instead
of easy-to-clean linoleum, and low ceilings that
force overgrown fellows like me into a permanent
stoop?

And it's not even a matter of 'learn to live with it.'
People seem to long for the way things used to be,
for 'the simple life.' I see this as basic faith in the
country tradition, a desire for harmony that comes
out especially in turbulent times.

I couldn't live in the country, and I wouldn't want to.
But who says you can't celebrate 'House & Garden' in
your two-bedroom city apartment?

Cynics scoff at this idyllic world as 'escapism.'
But doesn't that imply that the alternative is in a
sorry state?

Your dream of a simpler world, of honoring
tradition, doesn't have to be a pipe dream. Let the
impressions assembled in this chapter wash over
you, and I think you'll agree."

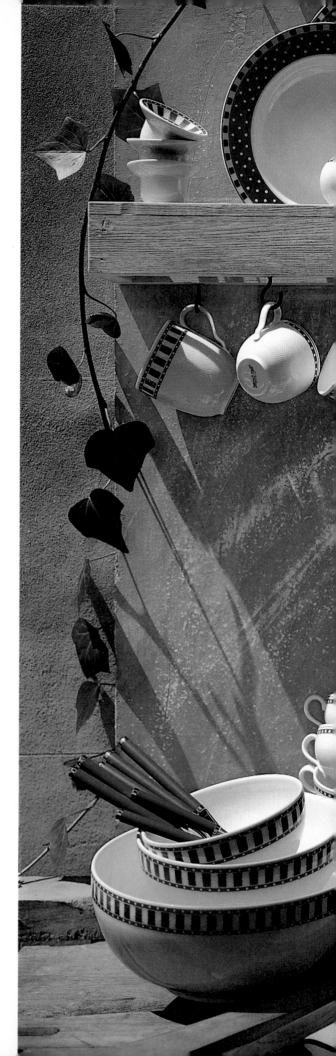

China: **PARTY LOOK**
Fine Vilbo China,
dishwasher safe.
Crystal: **AREZZO BLUE**
Cutlery: **PLAY!** green

41

** le secret of success.**

)ut here in the country, 'making it' isn't judged

 terms of money and possessions.

r me, success is mowing the bumpy lawn, hoeing

 e garden or picking the first apple of the season

 m my own tree.

 uess it all boils down to 'be yourself.'

 'e in the country makes you straightforward and

 actical-minded. Ostentation and frippery are

 cognized as what they are: nothing but show.

 u can't say that about 'Indian Look,' one of

 / favorite china patterns. The design was inspired

  traditional weaving patterns – in other words,

  the real thing."

China: INDIAN LOOK
Fine Vilbo China,
dishwasher safe.
Cutlery: TAO satin finish

Home sweet home.

"In today's modern world, the options are endless.
But does that necessarily mean we have to exercise
all of them?
Mobility is the major breakthrough of the
20th century. Meanwhile, we're starting to suspect
that happiness might be found right in our own
back yard.
For me as for many people, 'home sweet home'
is becoming an increasingly attractive alternative
to the big wide world out there – even though your
view may not be of the Mediterranean.
I say, just pack up and strike out for greener
pastures! Whether that means your very own
balcony, patio, garden
or rooftop."

China: BASKET
Vitreous China,
dishwasher safe.
Crystal: ALLEGORIE
Cutlery: PLAY! white

China: OLD LUXEMBOURG
Vitreous China,
dishwasher safe.
Cutlery: MERLEMONT

Yuppiedom is out.

When the '80s wheeler-dealers abandoned their highrises, we rediscovered something lost sight of amidst the empty glitter: a longing for tradition, a sense of history.

A thousand-mile journey always begins with a single step. For Villeroy & Boch, that step was the establishment of a ceramics factory in Lorraine on April 1st, 1748. Just a few decades later, the enterprise counted among the cream of European craftsmen and "Francois Boch et Frères, Manufacture Impériale et Royale" in Septfontaines, Luxembourg, was already catering to noble tastes.

For almost two and a half centuries, the company – which the world knows today as Villeroy & Boch, the first name in dining culture, tiles and sanitary ceramics – has travelled a path marked by milestone after milestone.

One of the very first: "Brindille," a late 18th century design, lives on today as "Old Luxembourg," a luminary in the Villeroy & Boch firmament.

China: **TIPO BLUE**
Fine Vilbo China,
dishwasher safe.
Crystal: **TORINO SPECIAL**
Cutlery: **PLAY! blue**

Compliments.

"When was the last time a guest gave you a compliment?

Not after the meal, but beforehand?

Let your answer inspire you – maybe it's time to entertain

a few fresh ideas.

All to better entertain your guests."

Sweet Sunday.

"I'm not afraid to admit it – outward appearances are important to me!

I like a table with a tablecloth. Even though it's not a matter of life and death – my tabletop is immaculate as it is.

But I'm a person who puts stock in custom and tradition. Sunday morning's for church, and Sunday dinner's a tablecloth affair.

And that's just the way I like it!"

Château

ollection

The start of a beautiful friendship.

"Hundreds of love stories wind up in a castle.
Mine begins in one: aux Château 'Outrelaise.'
Whatever mystery it holds, the name serenades
with the softness of velvet, a melodic portrait
reflecting the sweet symmetry of Renaissance
architecture.

A magical place whose sorcery lies in spurring
opulent occasions, festive flourishes and grand
gestures."

China: **VILLA ARTIMINO**
Bone China,
dishwasher safe.
Crystal: **DESIREE**
Cutlery: **SEPTFONTAINES**

La belle liaison.

"They say that understatement will be the design trend
of the future.

Why wait till then?

I have a feeling that patterns like 'Villa Adriana' have already
arrived at the charted destination.

You might call this timeless château style a liaison of simplicity
and elegance: classical, yet contemporary in feel."

China: VILLA ADRIANA
Bone China,
dishwasher safe.

Grandeur as large as life
is not always beyond your
wildest dreams.

China: VILLA MENTON
Bone China,
dishwasher safe.

To give credit where credit's due: Around two centuries ago, the amazing new properties exhibited by porcelain when mixed with bone ash are said to have been discovered by Josiah Spode the Second, of Stoke-on-Trent, England.

Since then, bone china has come to be seen as the embodiment of exquisite dining culture in every corner of the globe.

Which comes as no surprise to the connoisseurs. Though extremely fine, bone china is also extremely strong. Its remarkable translucent quality makes it a shimmering star in the porcelain firmament.

Bone china from Villeroy & Boch is considered the crème de la crème within this prestigious circle. Each piece of bone china in the Château Collection can be recognized by the Heinrich name, accompanied by the distinctive Heinrich colon.

Bone china services from Villeroy & Boch grace many an illustrious table. Just ask King Juan Carlos of Spain, Pope John Paul II, the Ducal Family of Luxembourg or Queen Beatrix of Holland.

So adorning your fine table in similar style puts you in good company. After all, bone china is something very special. But not especially expensive.

Elegance.

"Floral patterns are
among those classics with
an elegance that enhances
any environment.
Under the gilt ceilings
of a royal residence or in
a cozy breakfast corner –
a highlight like 'Columbia'
is always at home.
This was definitely a con-
sideration when deciding
on a wedding gift for
my niece. I chose this
bone china service – as a
symbol of eternal union,
of affection that doesn't
fade with time."

COLUMBIA
China,
asher safe.

Discerning tastes.

"In times when mediocrity is the norm, high standards are often interpreted as arrogance. But I think it's a mark of self-assurance to recognize second-best for what it is, and to reject it. In my opinion, bucking the trend and insisting on top quality is not a matter of money. It's not living in the lap of luxury that's important, but rather being in the know."

China: **LOUISIANA**
Bone China,
dishwasher safe.
Crystal: **OCTAVIE**
Cutlery: **ARLON**

Inner beauty.

" 'Only shallow people don't judge by appearances.' My sentiments exactly, in the words of the great Oscar Wilde. A master in all matters of an aesthetic nature, he had a well-developed sense of the role beauty plays in our lives. When judging the appearance of bone china, though, you might also want to go beneath the surface. Just hold a plate or saucer up to the light, and you'll discover the transparency that lends your china service its superb quality of lightness and elegance."

China: **PHILADELPHIA**
Bone China,
dishwasher safe.
Crystal: TORINO
Cutlery: LILIA

Château.

"The china we use says as much about us as the clothes we wear. Both speak volumes about our sense of style and what it's worth to us. They reveal whether we go with the flow or wander off the beaten track, whether we can laugh at ourselves or tend to take it all oh-so-seriously. The beautiful elements of a well-laid table also speak a distinct language, one that is easy to understand if you know the codes.

Color is one code – red comes across as self-confident, blue as sentimental – and shape is another. But labels are part of it, too: brand name, material, manufacturer, designer.

You might consider this the basic vocabulary for the language of 'Château.'

Cherishing tradition in times of indifference is a sign of self-possession.

'Château' embodies the aspiration to embrace beautiful rituals – such as fêting

very special days with festive china.

The revival of tradition – weddings, anniversaries, birthdays, but also those

precious everyday moments – and the desire to celebrate legacies are welcome

trends.

And the values now back in vogue are those of the Château Collection:

refinement, style and perfection. Every Château china pattern is a thing of

beauty, a miniature work of art on the brilliant white of bone china.

And if you'd like to set a special accent, just add 'Heinrich.'

More than just a name, Heinrich is a noble Villeroy&Boch line that

stands for 'Château' and

the pleasure it has in store."

China, from left:
VILLA MEDICI
VILLA VERDE
VILLA CAPRESE
VILLA MAGICA
All china
dishwasher safe.

Crystal: ANTONIA

Is the wine a "Château" too?

The grander the crû, the more critical the presentation. Served in Villeroy & Boch crystal, fine vintages become even more pleasing to the palate.

This is beauty to hold and to behold, crystal of remarkable color purity and a resounding full tone to tout every toast.

In flawless glasses such as these – pictured here are selections from the "Antonia" series – wine offers up its true essence. Each design is optimally crafted to bring out the color, bouquet and aroma of wine to the utmost.

Connoisseurs will also be happy to hear that the faultless design of Villeroy & Boch crystal extends to dishwasher-safe performance. And that many series come with an availability guarantee until the year 2005.

tle piece of heaven.

vision of harmony and tranquility includes the

e pot as perfection in form, the alter ego of the

sso machine and the hectic images it conjures up.

tever the punch its contents might pack, the

iner itself is the very picture of well-being and

ity.

his point I can't be swayed. No matter how hard

chrome-clad designer thermoses try to sell

ion over form."

: VILLA CANNES
China,
asher safe.
l: TORINO
y: MERLEMONT

The fabric of dreams.
From left:
FEDER
ESPLANADE ORIENTAL
ESPLANADE ARABESQUE

Cutlery: MONTGELAS

Even today, knives and forks are by no means a dire necessity for three-quarters of the world's population, who rely on chopsticks or simply use their fingers. For the remaining one in four, we have an important message.

Cutlery from Villeroy & Boch – which we recommend as ideal complements to series from the Château Collection – are worthy renditions of designs from the great style epochs since Medieval times.

Inspired by creations from the baroque, rococo, classicist and empire periods, Villeroy & Boch has paid tribute to design excellence through the ages. Its affinity for a modern spin on the Greats is backed by masterful craftsmanship and well-developed stylistic sensibility.

These cutlery classics are available in 18/10 stainless steel and 120 g silverplate, the latter a unique Villeroy & Boch offer containing a considerably higher silver concentration than the standard 90 g.

This recommendation to you reflects our higher ambition to be the first name in dining culture. In other words, your premier source of superior china, crystal and cutlery, too.

"Château": A sense
of style at table – right,
left and center.
Cutlery: SEPTFONTAINES

Magic.

"I believe in situational synergy.

– Could you run that by me again?

For instance, when coincidence brings two people

together, and suddenly chemistry kicks in. Sometimes

sparks fly, sometimes both are shaken to their very core.

It can happen with china, too.

The first time you set your table, you might just realize

that a special dynamic is at work.

And your hearth and home and Villeroy & Boch china

turn out to be a match made in heaven."

Paloma Pica

o Collection

"Paloma Picasso" – a sense
of style, a spark of creativity,
a penchant for the personal
touch.
China: CENTRAL PARK
Bone China, dishwasher safe.
Crystal: ROMA
Cutlery: AGRIGENTO
Napkin ring: AGRIGENTO

China: **PARK AVENUE**
Bone China, dishwasher safe.
Crystal: **VENEZIA**
Pitcher: **PALOMA PICASSO**
Cutlery: **AGRIGENTO**

Once upon a time, taste and trend were virtually one and the same. Personal flair took its cue from the signs of the times.

Aficionados of the latest, greatest new thing have it hard in today's post-modern world, as the universal longing for direction, clarity and distinction shows.

Which is what makes designers like Paloma Picasso so special – consummate artists who draw inspiration from their own creative wellspring, rather than endlessly mining the market of ideas.

Charisma is the source of Paloma Picasso's creative power, her signature style with its bold, unmistakable lines.

Her friend Yves Saint Laurent describes her as a woman with taste bred in the bone.

And Paloma Picasso cultivates this inborn talent to the utmost in her exclusive jewelry, perfume and accessories. And, last but not least, in her super-lative bone china, crystal and cutlery designs for Villeroy & Boch.

Surrounding yourself with these flawless objects is a way of expressing individual panache. Not to glorify material possessions, but rather to celebrate your very essence.

You can't buy
personality.
But you can show
your true colors.
With Paloma Picasso,
for instance.

A clear distinction.

"Some comparisons are apt – and valuable tools for measuring merit. When you ponder the benefits a BMW has to offer, don't you mull over the Mercedes? The first time you taste Persian caviar, don't your taste buds think back to beluga? When savoring Scotch, don't you bear bourbon in mind? In similar style, bone china should be held up to porcelain. What sets the former apart is its radiant whiteness, intense colors and delicate translucence. Trust your eyes."

Left:
Crystal: ROMA
VENEZIA

Right:
China: MADISON A
Bone China,
dishwasher safe.
Crystal: ROMA
Carafe: PALOMA P
Cutlery: CORDON

Typical Paloma Picasso:
crystal-clear contributions
to the world of design.

Occasions.

"'Possessions don't mean anything,' said my friend
in one of her philosophical moods. 'Unless you hold them
in your hands and put them to use.' I agree completely.
What's the point of owning the most exquisite china, but
never allowing it to enrich your life? Then it's nothing but
pretty wall decorations. Gathering dust, only truly enjoyed
once in a blue moon on those momentous occasions.
But life is too short and too precious to wait for special
occasions. Better to make them happen!
Another philosopher urges us to 'seize the day!'
Let me just add: to revel in the stunningly set table."

VIVA
China,
asher safe.
l: ROMA
y: PEARL
lly goldplated

MY WAY
China,
asher safe.
y: PEARL

Reaching for the stars.

"Society-watchers report that many a yuppie has changed into a 'puppy', i.e. poor urban professional! 'Sun, Moon & Stars' by Paloma Picasso provides daily inspiration to reach new heights!"

China:
SUN, MOON & STARS
Bone China,
dishwasher safe.
Cutlery: AGRIGENTO

"Switch" is for everyone
with an eye for variety and
a touch of dining-decor
genius!
China: SWITCH 4
Porcelain, dishwasher safe.
Glasses: SUNNY
Cutlery: PLAY! terracotta

China: **SWITCH 1**
Porcelain,
dishwasher safe.
Glasses: **SUNNY**
Cutlery: **ORLANDO**
satin finish

How many different china services does the average family keep in the buffet?

Statistics say 2.8.

With "Switch" in the picture, you can't possibly keep count – you're immediately spoilt for choice without spending a fortune.

That's because "Switch" is more than just an ordinary tableware range. "Switch appeal" showers you with imaginative ideas for spicing up life with patterns galore.

Go for perfect harmony or cool contrast – stripes with flowers, checks with solids, cheerful china for breakfast, romantic groupings for a candlelit evening.

With "Switch," your options are virtually endless when it comes to changing the scene.

Villeroy & Boch thinks of this exciting variation on the art of the well-laid table as "porcelain made personal."

So go ahead – turn the tables to your heart's content! Though the switchover is never the same twice, it's always unique and attractive – and always a reflection of you.

Mix & Match.

"'Real style is constantly reinventing itself.'
So says my style-minded friend.
In like style, let me make a case for a playful approach
to the 'eternal,' often all-too-staid values.
'Anything goes' shouldn't be taken to mean 'whatever.'
It should spark your desire to start thinking 'Switch' —
mixing and matching colors, shapes and patterns."

China: **SWITCH 3**
Porcelain,
dishwasher safe.
Glasses: **SUNNY BLUE**
Cutlery: **ORLANDO**
satin finish

The brighter, the better.
The big, brilliant, beautiful
world of "Switch."
From left:
COLORE
with leaf pattern
GARDEN
COLORE with speckled
pattern
FARO
COLORE with piping
COLORE with embroidered
edging

Creature comforts.

"I'm a homebody, I admit it. It's just that I prefer lounging contentedly on my balcony to haunting the latest local hotspot.

The trend pundits call it 'cocooning' – an increasing devotion to the comforts of home rather than the insistent beat of the urban jungle.

I call it comfort. It's a feeling, a way of life whose siren call I follow above all else."

Top:
Vases: JAVA

Bottom:
Vase: ALGARVE
Salad bowl:
SALATPARTY ALGARVE

CI

Cam

TÀ

agna

Home is where the heart is.

"The new 'homecoming' trend isn't about rediscovering the joys of drawing room decor and century-old settees.

To me, coziness and comfort are anything fun, easygoing and spontaneous. Like lingering at the dinner table for hours, putting another pot of coffee on and making room for a second helping of pie.

Followed by the ultimate convenience: simply stashing everything in the dishwasher."

China: NOVI
Porcelain,
dishwasher safe.
Cutlery: PLAY! blue/green

China: BIELLA
Porcelain,
dishwasher safe.
Glasses: DONAU

In the 18th century, Prince Elector August the Strong purchased 120 pieces of white gold at the price of nearly 600 Saxon dragoons. In that day and age, a single porcelain terrine would have cost one of his subjects at least three months' wages.

Even today, some hand-painted pieces are not to be had for less than the proverbial arm and leg. Certain china services could even share price tags with a C-class Mercedes!

But that doesn't have to be the case. Villeroy & Boch offers an attractive alternative with its "Città & Campagna" collection because it likes to share the pleasure of porcelain – at affordable prices.

"Città & Campagna" in
one of its natural habitats.
All the comforts of home –
with contemporary charm.
China: ASCOLI
Porcelain,
dishwasher safe.
Glasses: DONAU
Cutlery: PLAY! red

China: CASTELLINA
Porcelain,
dishwasher safe.
Cutlery: PLAY! yellow

Kitchen coziness.

"City and country – if the former has borrowed something from the latter, it's an atmosphere of friendly intimacy, like on those occasions when everyone gathers around a big wooden table to enjoy homemade hospitality. Feasting on roast chicken and thick mashed potatoes, green beans and steaming-hot rolls – not to mention a thick slice of rich chocolate cake! No sign of cold modern design. The mood is set by the style we call 'Città & Campagna' – hearty fare, simple touches, a casual feel. Just my style!"

China: DESCO
Porcelain,
dishwasher safe.
Glasses: DONAU
Cutlery: PLAY! te

ATTRA

CTIONS

The art of catching the eye.

"People have always insisted that good things come in small packages.

From the cultural connoisseurs to the gurus of good taste, all agree that the fine details are just as important as the basics, that accessories pack great expressive power.

My trend-conscious friend calls it the 'earring' effect: small detail, big impact!

Crystal has the same power over the well-laid table – as finishing touch with a touch of genius!"

Crystal, from left:
PALOMA PICASSO
DOVER
TORINO
VERDI
CCC
INKA
Mocca cups:
CARROUSEL NOSTALGIE,
from Heinrich.

 PLATANO

RIO
bowls:
-BUFFET

eholders: SIENA
: PACIFIC
e frame: PRISMA

Class act.

"The sultans of style tell us
that the pendulum has swung
back the other way – the era
of lavish, luxury-obsessed
living is history. I don't mind
as long as this age of 'new
frugality' ends up looking like
these accessories. No room
for the superfluous. But
plenty of room for class!"

ANIMAL PARK: "Froggy"

Ever since Spencer Tracy shuffled across the screen as the downcast father of the bride, hair dishevelled and battered check book in tow, we've known one thing for certain: getting married isn't cheap!

And the straits are often just as dire for those not bearing the costs of the Big Day. After all, they bear the burden of gift selection.

Heartfelt though a gift may be, the problem is, there's no guarantee it will win the heart of the lucky recipient.

Almost everyone can empathize with the soul-stirring lament: "Whatever am I going to get them?"

Villeroy & Boch recommends its selection of "wedding dream gifts" for all those dreading the gift-giver's dilemma.

Available from your local retailer, this is a treasure trove of inspired gift ideas for everyone bemoaning the fate of the wedding well-wisher.

Whether the dream gift you have in mind is an enhancement for the art of dining – china services, glassware, cutlery – or an exquisite accessory like a candleholder, picture frame, vase or figurine.

The key word to remember is "Attractions" – attractive gift ideas for beautiful homes.

ël.

hen it's time to deck halls and stuff stockings,

e spirit of giving has traditionally gone for a

nventional choice.

ough taking a fun, original approach might just

rease yuletide joy that much more.

ahead and ring in the Feast of Feasts with our

yful "Christmas Ornaments," modern makeovers

the traditional tree decoration.

Left:
China: MAGIC CHRISTMAS
Bone China, dishwasher safe.
Crystal: ALLEGORIE

Above:
CHRISTMAS ORNAMENTS

Cultural exchange.

"I'm a big fan of the variety of life. I like to try lots of different things on for size, all depending on how the spirit moves me. Since my tastes are so eclectic, swimming against the latest fashion current isn't a problem. And going your own way is really worth it. Otherwise I'd never have met my friends from the heart-warming world of 'Foxwood!'"

Foxwood Tales

The last word.

This book in celebration of an internationally acclaimed brand
and the ambience it evokes was made possible by the excellent
contributions of many people.
The photos came from Brigitte Richter, Nicolas Bruant,
Achim Deimling-Ostrinsky, Jean Louis Mennesson,
Markus Meuthen, Gerd Spans and Helmut Winterfeld.
Text, layout and organization were masterminded by the
Struwe & Partner team of Gerd Fehling, Ursula Craemer,
Andreas Fußhöller and Josi Dörflinger.
The project was spearheaded by Wendelin von Boch and
Günter Mann, both of Villeroy & Boch, and Gerd Fehling.

Villeroy & Boch AG
Unternehmensbereich Tischkultur
Postfach 10 00 27
66652 Merzig
Germany
Tel.: +49 6864/814-040